For Alma, Lyla, Rafi and Coby

Published in the UK by Scholastic, 2022
Euston House, 24 Eversholt Street, London, NW1 1DB
Scholastic Ireland, 89E Lagan Road, Dublin Industrial Estate, Glasnevin, Dublin, D11 HP5F

SCHOLASTIC and associated logos are trademarks and/or
registered trademarks of Scholastic Inc

Text © Leanne Miller, 2022
Illustrations © Sara Miller Design Ltd., 2022

The right of Leanne Miller and Sara Miller Design Ltd. to be identified as the author and illustrator
of this work has been asserted by them under the Copyright, Designs and Patents Act 1988.

HB ISBN 978 07023 1165 9
PB ISBN 978 07023 1363 9

A CIP catalogue record for this book is available from the British Library.

Printed in China
Paper made from wood grown in sustainable forests and other controlled sources.

1 3 5 7 9 10 8 6 4 2

Party
Parade

Leanne Miller   Sara Miller

SCHOLASTIC

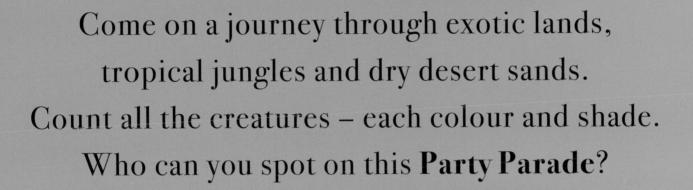

Come on a journey through exotic lands,
tropical jungles and dry desert sands.
Count all the creatures – each colour and shade.
Who can you spot on this **Party Parade**?

1

One wonderfully wise and worldly blue whale
splishing and splashing his beautiful tail.
Look amongst the bright seabed – can you see
one small seahorse sipping a cup of tea?

2

Two sleepy sloths snuggling up in their tree,
swinging *s l o w l y* through leafy canopies.
Look through the luscious lemons, take a peek.
Find the green lizard playing hide-and-seek!

3

Three gleeful geese *cha-cha-cha-ing* in line,
necks upright, heads turned back, feet move in time.
Can you spot their spotty friends, one, two, three,
watching the bunnies bouncing playfully?

4

Four fine frogs wearing bow ties and top hats,
leaping off lily pads – such charming chaps!
Cool cat cruising by, lounging in the sun.
Mousey's rowing hard, but where's Mousey's Mum?

5

Five flamboyant flamingos frolicking by
lush green palms and a pink tropical sky.
Carrying watermelons, oh-so sweet!
Who has *swooped* by and *swiped* a tasty treat?

6

Six slender camels guided by the moon,
all in bright colours, stars twinkling on the dunes.
Wearing jewelled crowns, across the sand they stride.
Find the dusty desert mouse hitching a ride!

7

Seven stylish lemurs sweeping through trees.
Up, down, round they go, playing with such ease.
Happily hanging out, what a buoyant bunch!
Spy one picking a banana for lunch.

8

Eight iguanas camouflaged in the leaves,
soaking in the sun's rays, still in the breeze.
In this kingdom, where many creatures roam,
spot a butterfly, fluttering by, on her own.

9

Nine proud penguins gather in the white snow,
little one skates with a snowman in tow.
By the misty mountains, where snowflakes fall,
find the trail of footprints, dainty and small.

10

Ten friendly creatures arrive at the ball,
tortoise trails *s l o w l y* as giraffe stands **tall**.
The Party Parade's led by a graceful deer.
Our counting's complete, give yourself a **cheer**!

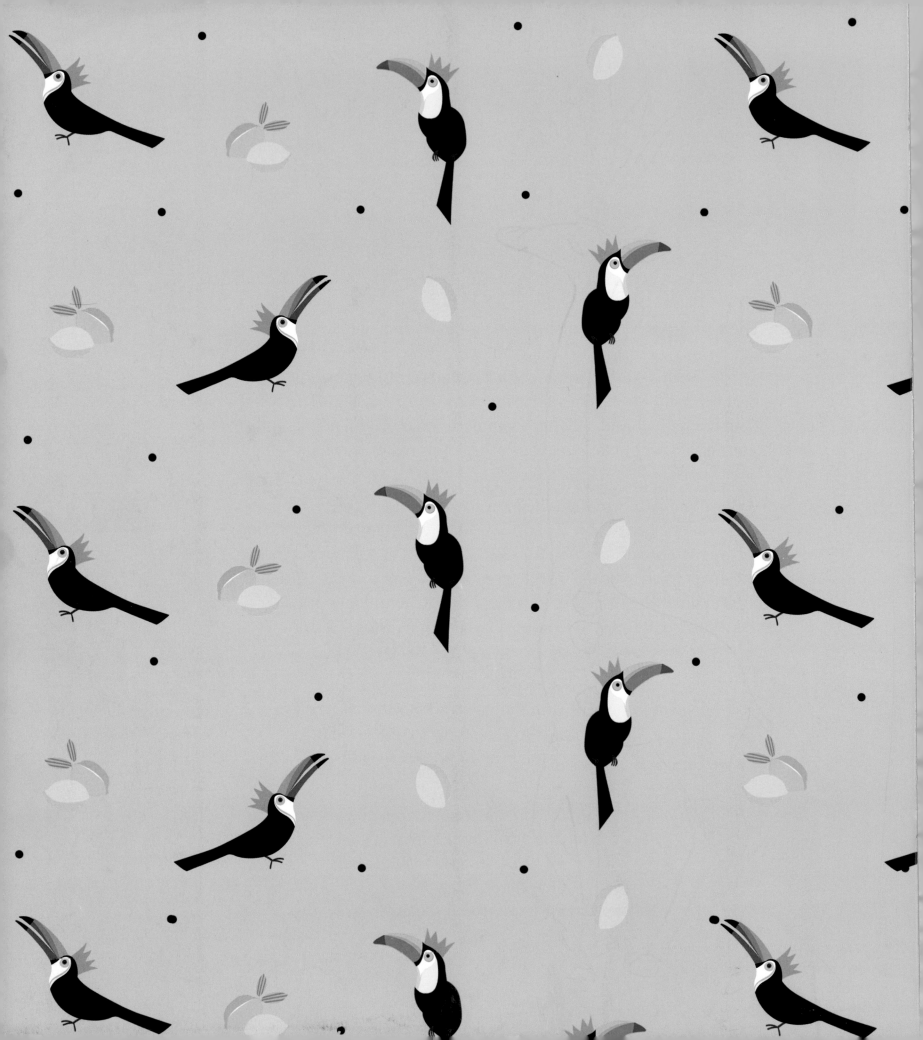

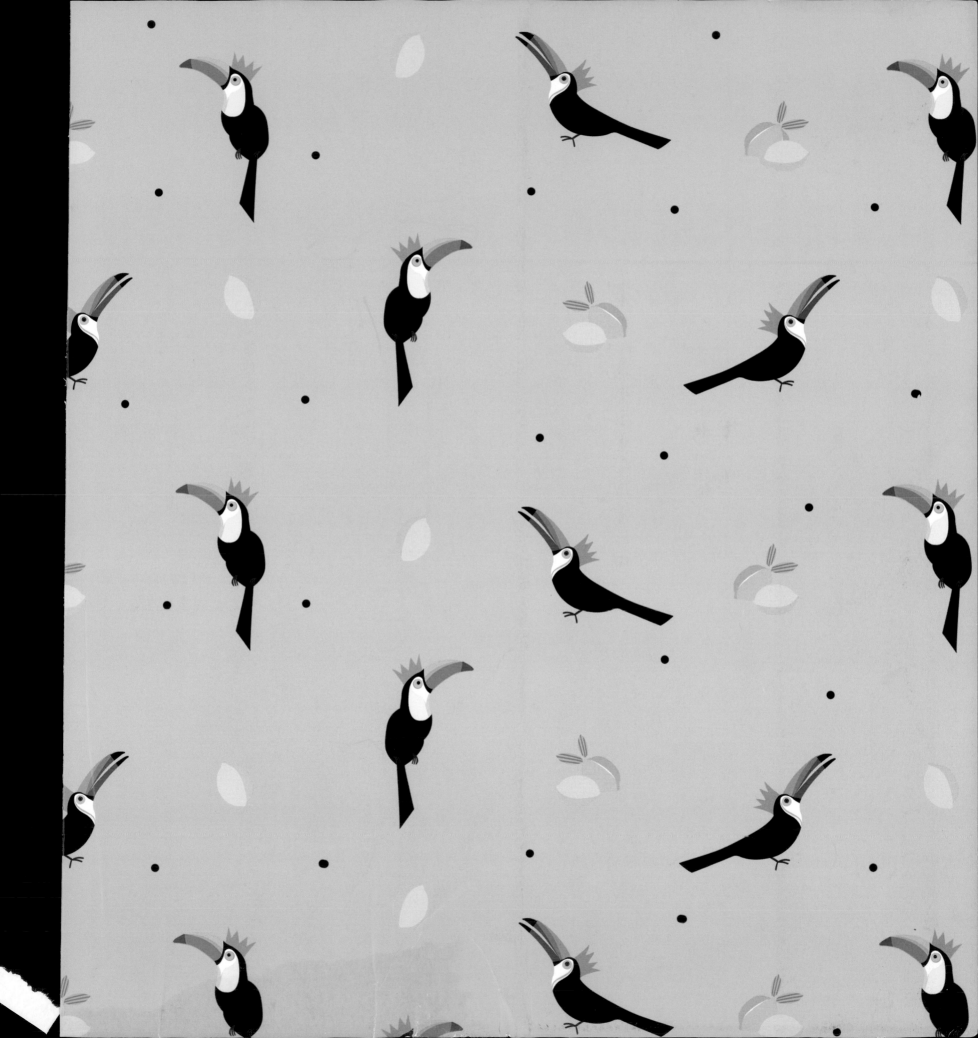